Judith Crist, whose snappy reviews for stupid movies have made her one of the most reliable reviewers around, has this to say about ''Mad's Al Jaffee Spews Out MORE Snappy Answers to Stupid Questions:''

What can you say about a 192 page book that _lives_! That it's a masterpiece. Sensational. Superb. That it's a trend-setter. That it will garner 10 National Book Award nominations. That it's a smash. That it should only make $100 million. You can say it. All _I_ can say is I'm sorry.

Love,

Judith Crist

MAD'S
AL JAFFEE
SPEWS OUT
MORE
SNAPPY ANSWERS
TO
STUPID QUESTIONS

WRITTEN AND ILLUSTRATED BY AL JAFFEE

EDITED BY ALBERT B. FELDSTEIN
WITH A FORWARD BY NICK MEGLIN

WARNER BOOKS

A Warner Communications Company

Dedication

To the people at Mad who made it possible, and the people at the Internal Revenue Service who made it *necessary!*

Warner Books, Inc.
666 Fifth Avenue
New York, N.Y. 10103

 A Warner Communications Company

Printed in the United States of America

First Warner Books Printing: April, 1979

Reissued: October, 1984

10 9 8 7 6 5 4 3

Al Jaffee:
The Man Behind the Legend
by Nick Meglin

(An exclusive interview with the author/illustrator of
"Mad's Al Jaffee Spews Out Snappy Answers to Stupid
Questions" and "The Mad Book of Magic and Other
Dirty Tricks")

Few of us come close to greatness. Even fewer come
close to Al Jaffee! And the reason is simple—no one
particularly *wants* to come close to him! Why? Because
he gives out with *snappy answers!* All the time, snappy answers! God forbid you should ask him a question!
Even a *smart* question! He comes out with a snappy
answer and makes you feel stupid! So you can imagine

how it was to *interview* him! Because to interview, you *gotta* ask questions . . .

N.M.: Is this book a sequel to "Snappy Answers to Stupid Questions"?
A.J.: No, it's a sequel to the Bible!
N.M.: Was the first book a success?
A.J.: No, it was a failure! They *always* do sequels of failures!
N.M.: Was it difficult coming up with entirely new situations and gags?
A.J.: No, it was easier! It's always easier after you've done it all and there's nothing left to write about!
N.M.: Did you do the drawings for this one as well?
A.J.: No, Rembrandt did the drawings! He just signed them "Jaffee" to fool his friends!
N.M.: Do you always spew out snappy answers?
A.J.: No, only to stupid questions! And so far, you've topped them all!
N.M.: Would you think me rude if I punched you in the stomach?
A.J.: No, I'd think you rude if you punched me in the nose!
N.M.: Okay, have it your way—
A.J.: OOOOF!

"SNAPPY ANSWERS
TO STUPID
QUESTIONS"

8

9

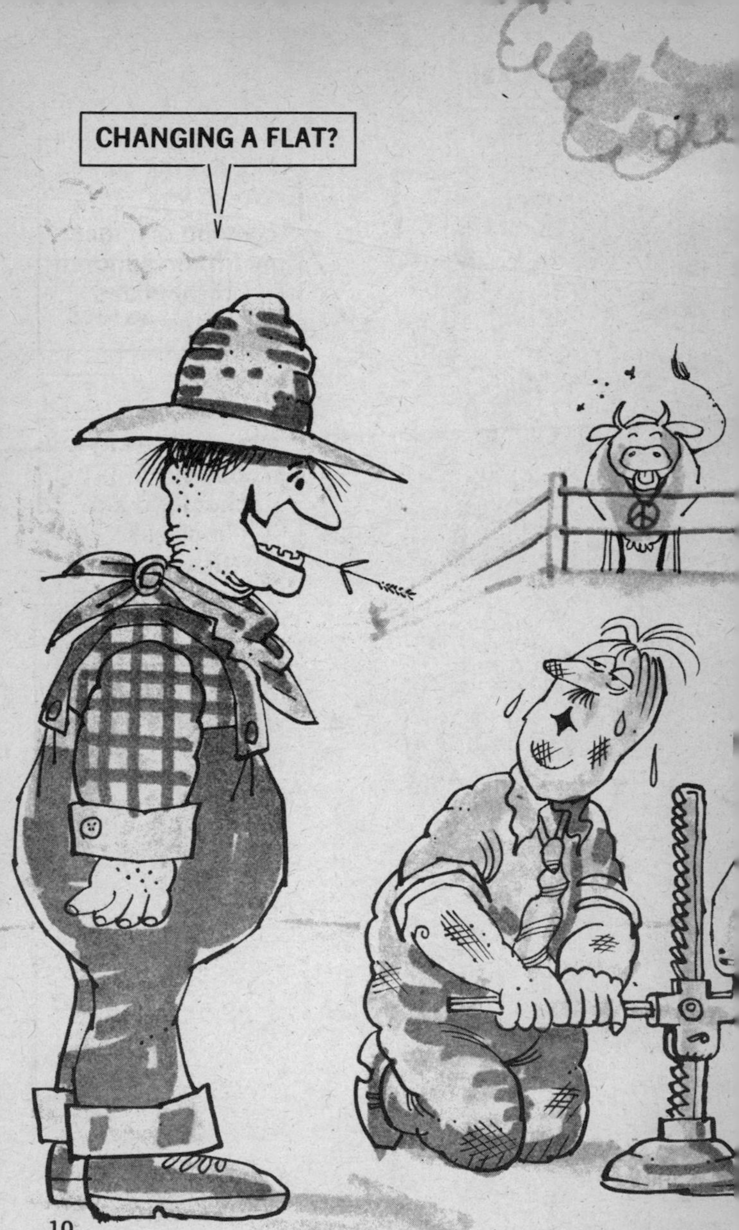
CHANGING A FLAT?

11

13

14

16

17

A "SNAPPY ANSWERS TO STUPID QUESTIONS" DESERT ISLAND SAGA

MORE "SNAPPY ANSWERS TO STUPID QUESTIONS"

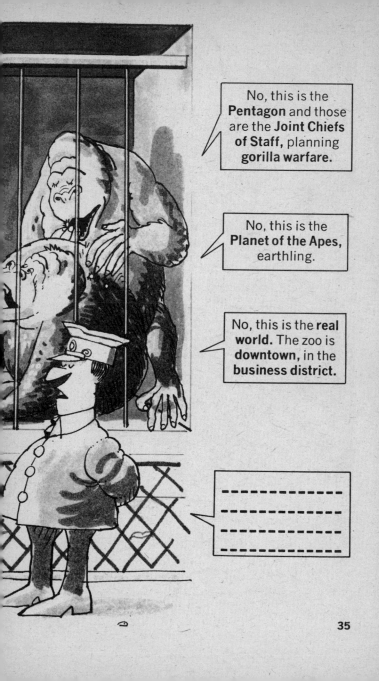

35

38

39

40

A "SNAPPY ANSWERS TO STUPID QUESTIONS" COPS AND ROBBERS STORY

46

BANK

BANK

47

49

51

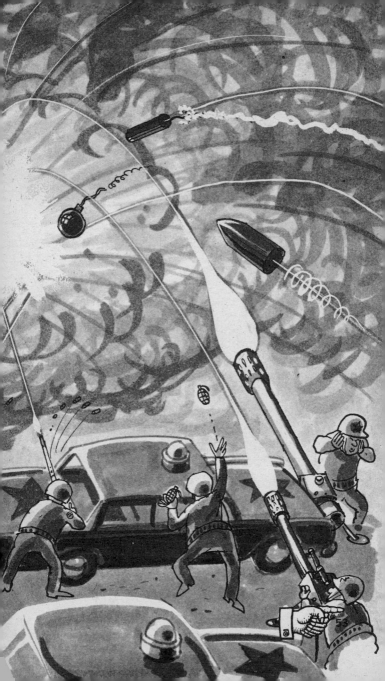

55

STILL MORE "SNAPPY ANSWERS TO STUPID QUESTIONS"

58

59

63

65

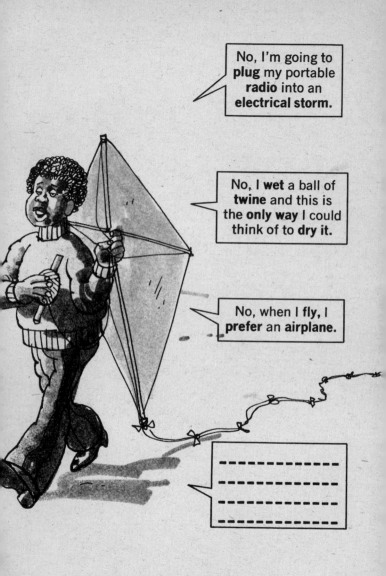

67

A "SNAPPY ANSWERS
TO STUPID
QUESTIONS"
GOLF STORY

70

72

73

74

75

76

77

78

79

BACK TO MORE OF THOSE (YECCH) "SNAPPY ANSWERS TO STUPID QUESTIONS"

THIS PICTURE RATED X
Only if accompanied by an adult pervert!
Only if they wear earmuffs and face the rear of the theater.
Yes, you'll need them to explain what's going on!
NO ONE UNDER 18 ADMITTED

85

This is **Friday,** but we like **Tuesday** so much we keep it **all week!**

This is **our lucky day** meeting someone as **observant** and **intelligent as you!**

It's "National Stupid Questions Day" and you win first prize.

\- \- \- \- \- \- \- \- \- \- \-
\- \- \- \- \- \- \- \- \- \- \-
\- \- \- \- \- \- \- \- \- \- \-
\- \- \- \- \- \- \- \- \- \- \-

88

90

A POETIC "SNAPPY
ANSWERS TO STUPID
QUESTIONS"

96

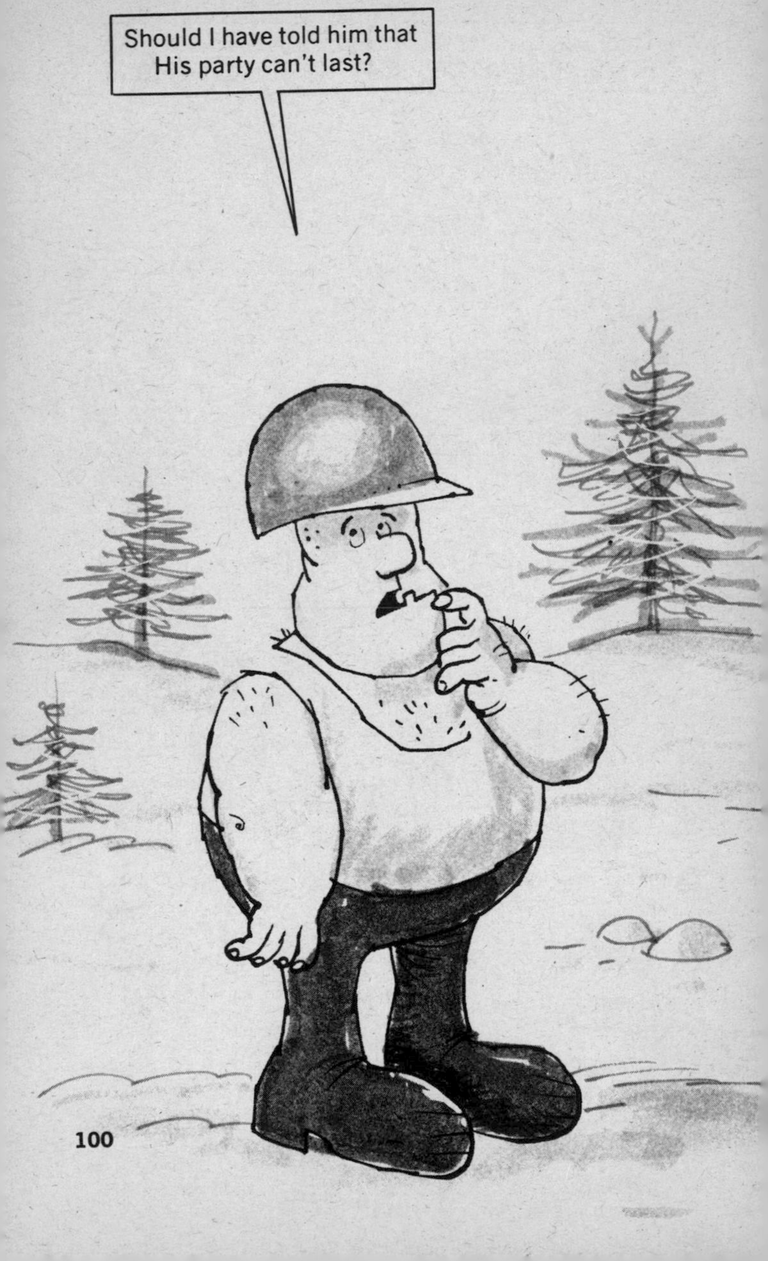
Should I have told him that
His party can't last?

DANGER
HIGHWAY
CONSTRUCTION

BACK TO STILL MORE OF THOSE (YECCH) "SNAPPY ANSWERS TO STUPID QUESTIONS"

107

My mother is a pink flamingo!
I stand on my head a lot and the blood stains my hair!
I eat two hundred carrots a day.

No, I'll **wait** till it **melts** and then I'll **drink it.**
No, I need **two slices of bread.** I meant to order an **ice cream sandwich.**
No, I need a **memo pad.** I want to make a **note** of the **superb service** in this place.

115

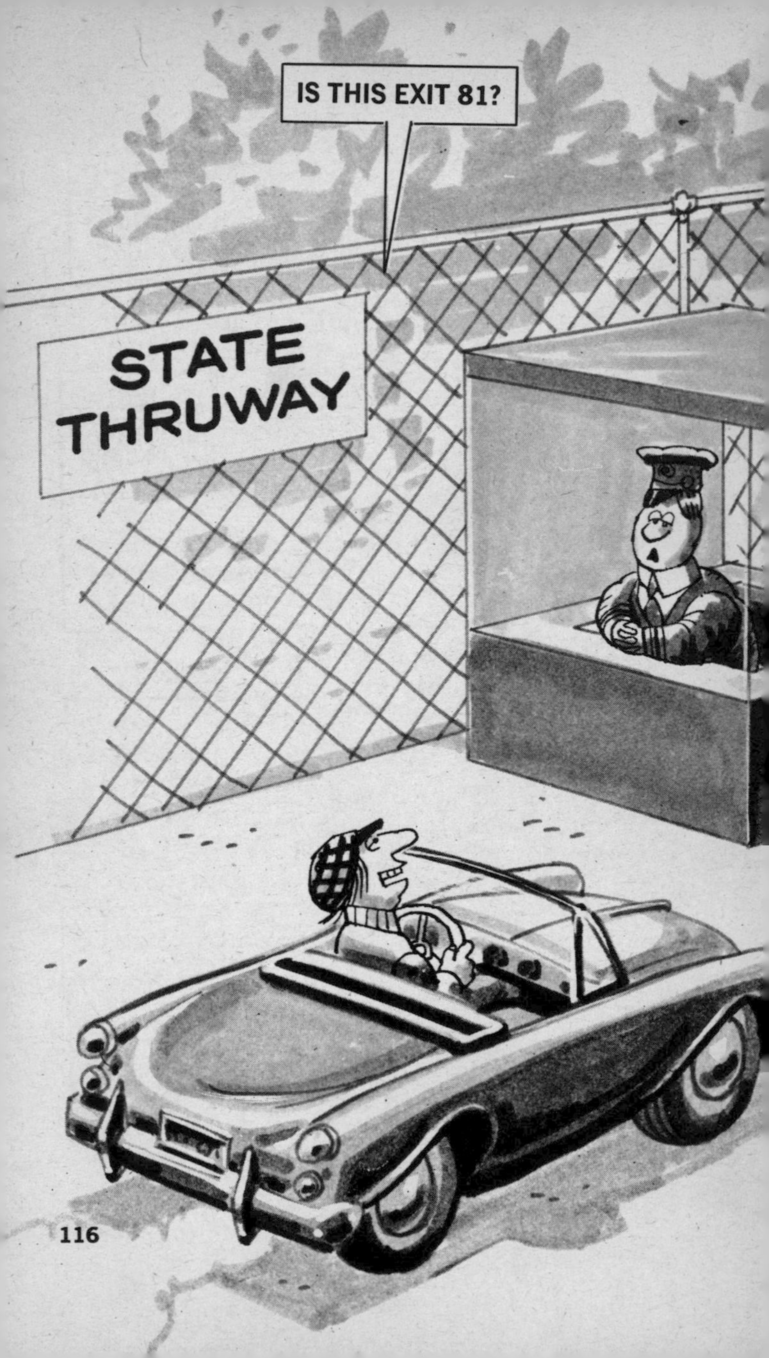
IS THIS EXIT 81?
STATE THRUWAY

EXIT 81
Sorry sir, I **don't know how old** this **exit** is—I'm **32** if that's **any help!**
No, that **big sign** is for **keeping count** of how many **stupid questions** I get asked **in a day.** Now, if you'll **excuse me,** I have to put up an **82.**
No, you have to take a number to get out, and we're up to 81 now!

"SNAPPY ANSWERS TO STUPID QUESTIONS" IN FANTASY LAND

120

121

123

124

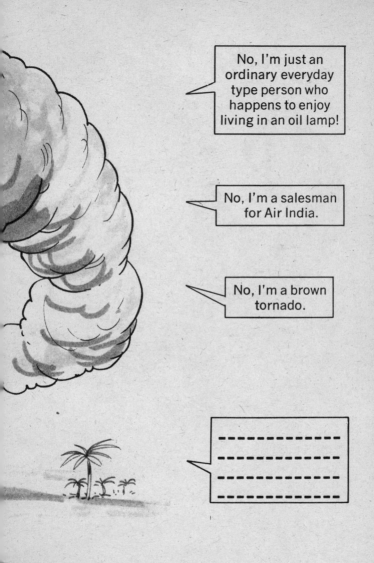

125

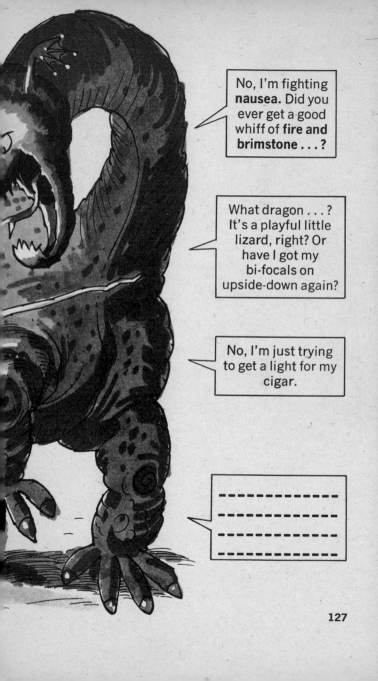

127

STINGING
COMEBACKS
TO "SNAPPY
ANSWERS TO
STUPID QUESTIONS"

ANYTHING BREAKABLE IN HERE?
No, "FRAGILE" means "MADE OF STEEL" in Swahili!
PARCEL POST
OUT OF TOWN
LOCAL
FRAGILE
FRAGILE
FRAGILE

131

IS THAT A GUN? No, it's a football.

Perdamaian

132

133

134

136

137

139

140

RETURNING (BLECCH) ONCE AGAIN TO THOSE (YECCH) "SNAPPY ANSWERS TO STUPID QUESTIONS"

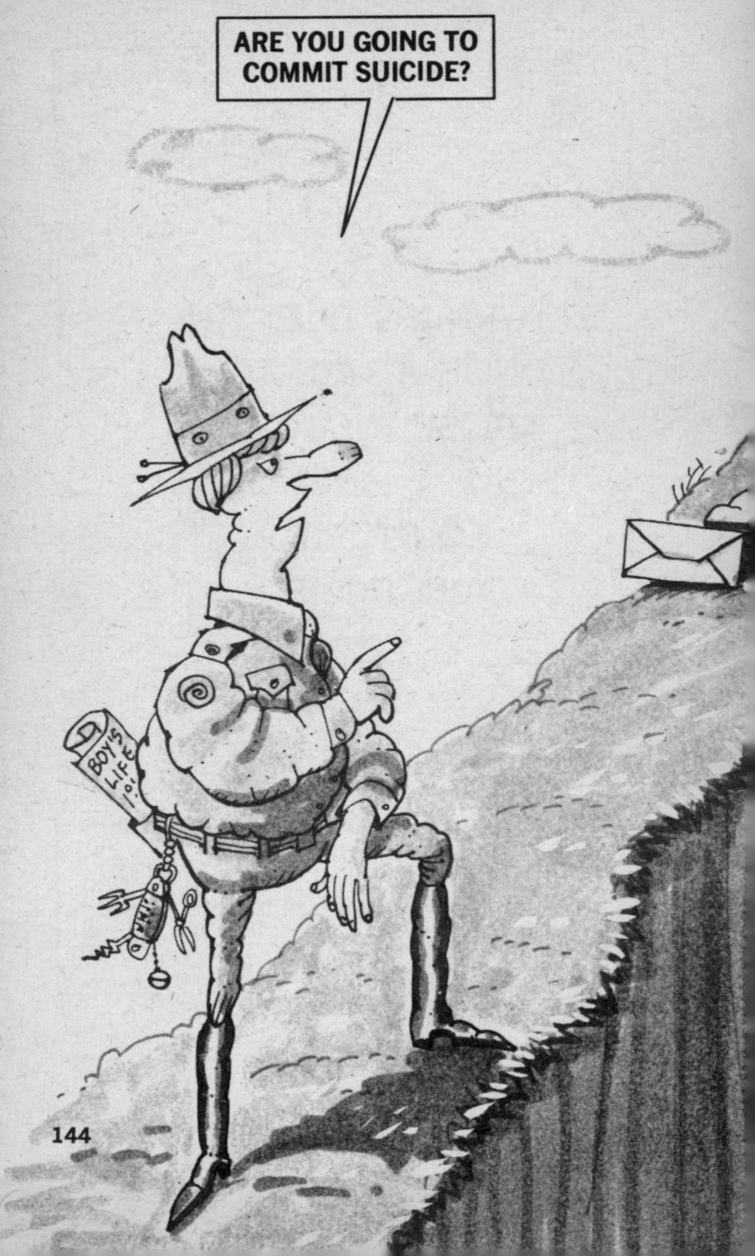
ARE YOU GOING TO COMMIT SUICIDE?
BOY'S LIFE

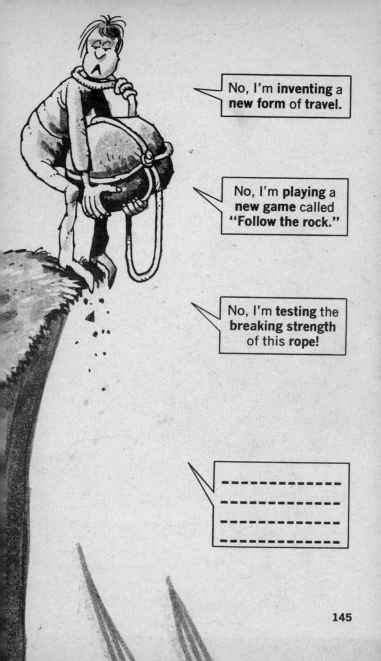

No, it's a **new type** inconspicuous **hearing aid.**

No, I was having **stomach trouble** so they **replaced my insides** with these **brass guts.**

No, it's a python. Stick your head in its mouth and it'll say something to you.

\- - - - - - - - - - - - -
\- - - - - - - - - - - - -
\- - - - - - - - - - - - -
\- - - - - - - - - - - - -

147

148

149

153

154

SOME "SNAPPY ANSWERS TO STUPID QUESTIONS" YOU'D BETTER KEEP TO YOURSELF

Course not. But if you p-p-pull him back a bit I can get a better view of the magnificent animal that he is.

No, but you'd better **call him off.** I'm afraid **my bad breath** might **offend him!**

Of **course** not! It's been my **lifelong ambition** to become a **gourmet meal** for a **St. Bernard.**

Dogs, no! But where did you get this **dinosaur?**

159

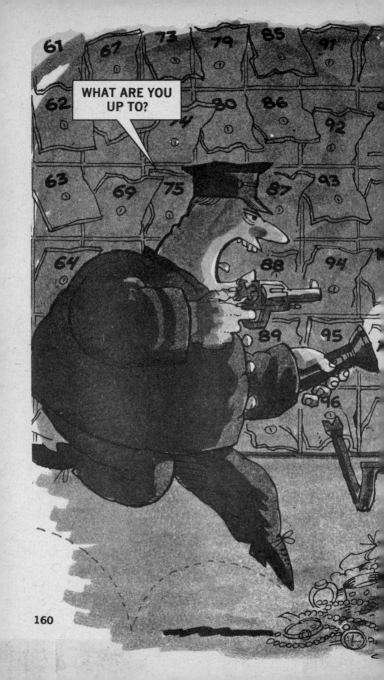

160

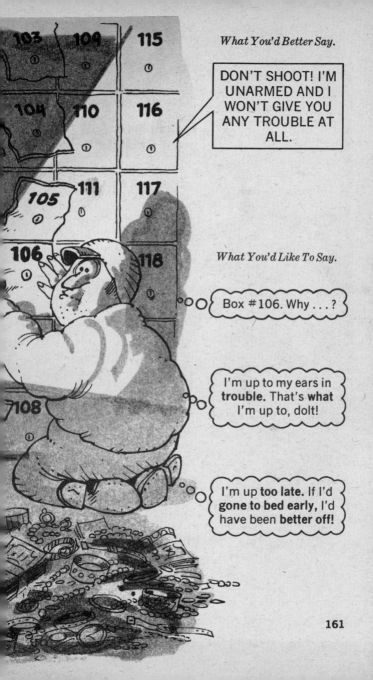

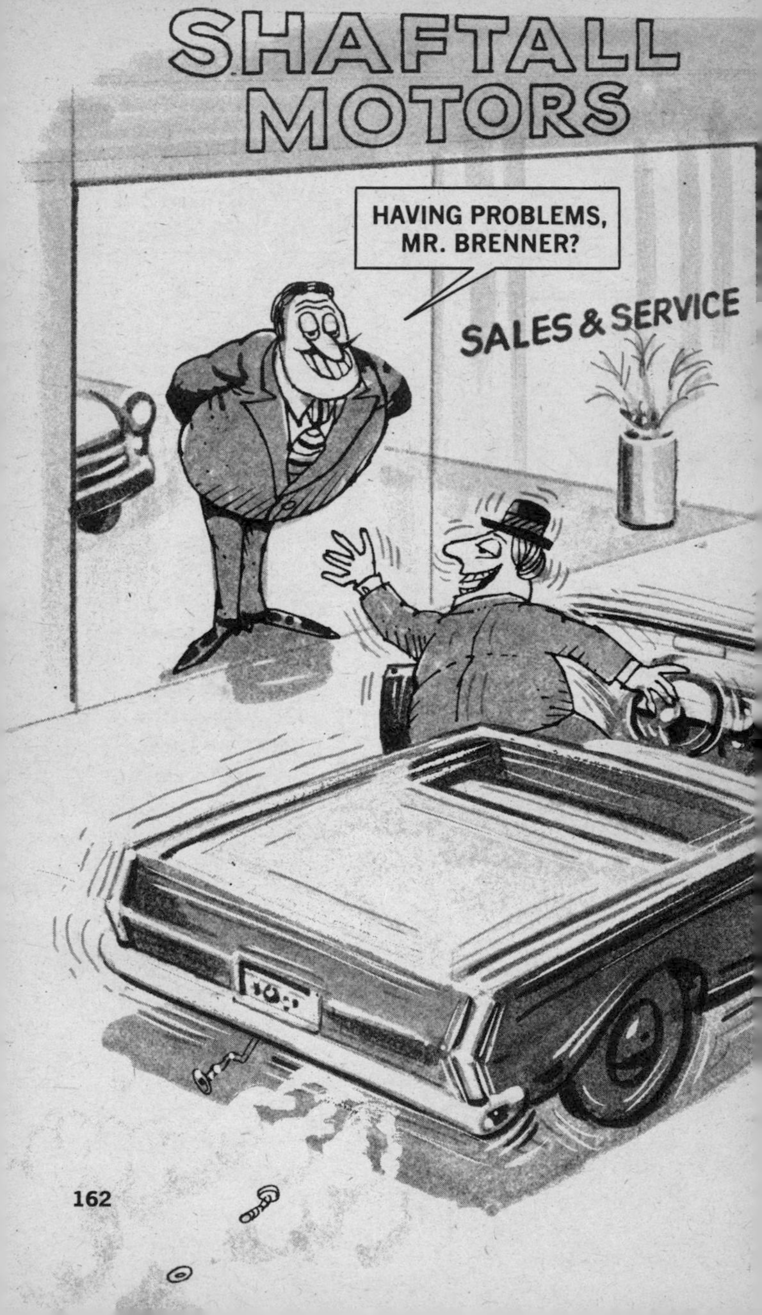
SHAFTALL MOTORS
HAVING PROBLEMS, MR. BRENNER?
SALES & SERVICE

What You'd Better Say.

Oh, nothing your skilled mechanics can't take care of in a jiffy, Mr. Shaftall.

What You'd Like To Say.

Problems. Oh, you mean that **trail of parts** the car leaves **wherever I go?** That's **no** problem. That's a **marvelous help** when I have to **find my way home again!**

Not **yet,** but after **I kill you** for selling me this **lemon,** I **will** have!

No, I **enjoy** people shouting "**get a horse!**" at me.

163

164

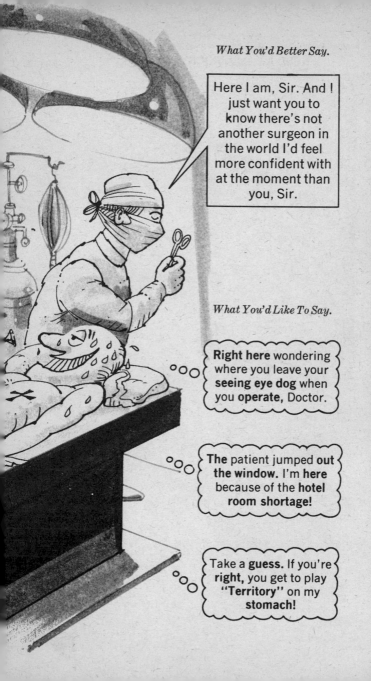

166

What You'd Better Say.

Yes, Tony, and p-p-please hurry, you wonderful beautiful human being you.

What You'd Like To Say.

No, just **catch me** when I **bounce back up!**

No, I want **you** to go down **on the street** and **warn people** to get **out of the way** of my **plunging body!**

No, just **remove** my new steel hat. I wouldn't want it dented should I be clumsy enough to land head-first!

167

169

170

What You'd Better Say.

Yes, and to save time and bother I've already selected what I want from my neighbor's menu.

ЯAUAT23Я

What You'd Like To Say.

No, I satisfy **my hunger** by watching **others** eat.

What, and **waste** my **lunch hour?**

Eat? Oh, my goodness, then **this** is **not** the **Public Library?**

What You'd Better Say.

Yes, please, mister —If I could just trouble you for the life preserver.

What You'd Like To Say.

No, **I'm practicing** for the Olympic **drowning** team

No, I think I can **swallow this ocean** all by myself.

Yes, I've lost **count.** Would you let me know **when** I've gone down for the **third time?**

AT LAST! THE LAST OF THOSE (YECCH) "SNAPPY ANSWERS TO STUPID QUESTIONS"

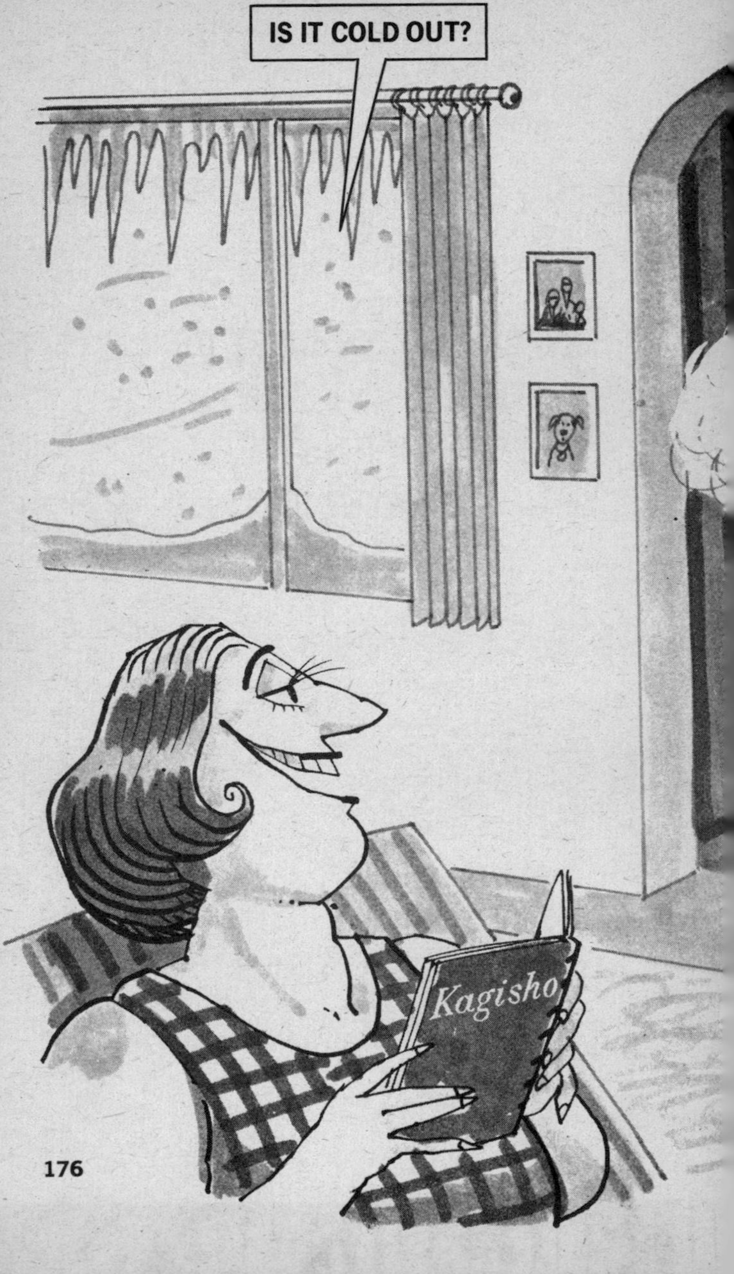
IS IT COLD OUT?
Kagisho

177

178

No, I'm **lonely** and this is the **only way** I can get to **meet people.**

For **information,** try **encyclopedias, third floor!**

Are you trying to **stump** me?

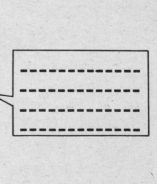

- - - - - - - - - - -
- - - - - - - - - - -
- - - - - - - - - - -
- - - - - - - - - - -

183

184

185

186

No, I just have long flowing **nose hairs.**

No, it's my **pet caterpillar.**

No, I'm growing a **lip brow!**

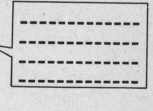

A 'HE WHO LAUGHS
LAST LAUGHS BEST'
"SNAPPY ANSWERS
TO STUPID
QUESTIONS"

190